Contents

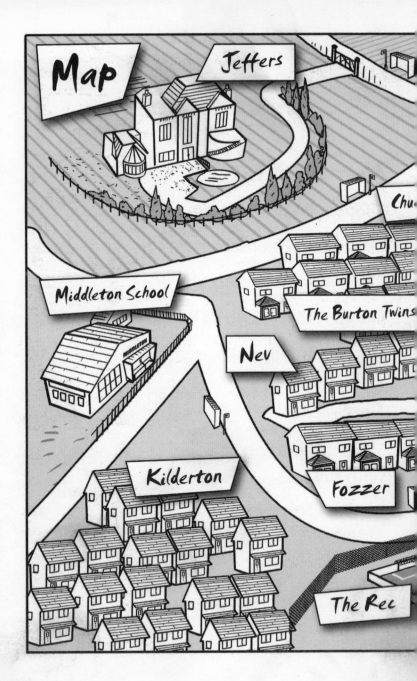

Map

Jeffers

Chu...

Middleton School

The Burton Twins

Nev

Kilderton

Fozzer

The Rec

4

THE JAGS

Your Turn in Goal

TOM WATT

RISING★STARS

Rising Stars UK Ltd.
22 Grafton Street, London W1S 4EX
www.risingstars-uk.com

Text, design and layout © 2009 Rising Stars Uk Ltd.
The right of Tom Watt to be identified as the author of this work has been
asserted by him in accordance with the Copyright, Design and Patents Act,
1988.

Published 2009

Publisher: Gill Budgell
Editor: Jane Wood
Text design and typesetting: Clive Sutherland
Illustrator: Michael Emmerson for Advocate Art
Cover design: Burville-Riley Partnership
Cover photograph: Ron Coello at www.coellophotography.co.uk
With special thanks to; Robert Dye, Harry Garner, Tyrone Smith, Lewis
McKenzie, Kobina Crankson and Alex Whyte

British Library Cataloguing in Publication Data.
A CIP record for this book is available from the British Library.

ISBN: 978-1-84680-482-3

Printed in the UK by CPI Bookmarque, Croydon, CR0 4TD

Mixed Sources
Product group from well-managed
forests and other controlled sources
www.fsc.org Cert no. TT-COC-002227
© 1996 Forest Stewardship Council

Meet the Jags

Name: Andrew Burton

Fact: He's the Jags' captain.

Loves: Spurs

FYI: The Jags may be his mates, but they'd better not forget he's the Skipper.

Name: Terry Burton

Fact: He's Andy's twin brother.

Loves: Football, football, and more football. He's football crazy!

FYI: He's a big Arsenal fan.

Name: Ryan Devlin

Fact: He's very forgetful.

Loves: Daydreaming!

FYI: He's always covered in mud and bruises.

Fozzer

Name: Hamed Foster

Fact: He can run like crazy, but he shoots like crazy too – sometimes at the wrong goal!

Loves: Telling bad jokes.

FYI: His best friend is Nev.

Keeps

Name: Jim Ward

Fact: He's the Jags' Number One goalie – whether he likes it or not!

Loves: Trying to score from his end of the pitch.

FYI: He's the tallest member of the Jags.

Jeffers

Name: Jeffrey Gilfoyle Chapman

Fact: He's the only one of the Jags who doesn't live on the Chudley Park estate.

Loves: Being in the Jags.

FYI: He's the Jags' top goal-scorer.

Nev

Name: Denton Neville

Fact: Nev is the Jags' most talented player.

Loves: Fozzer's bad jokes.

FYI: He keeps his feet on the ground and always looks out for his football crazy mates.

Mrs Burton

Name: Pam Burton

Fact: The Burton twins' mum, and a team 'mum' for all the Jags.

Loves: Sorting out her boys.

FYI: Doesn't actually like football!

Mr Ward

Name: Jack Ward

Fact: He's Jim's dad and the Jags' coach!

Loves: Going on and on, doing his team talks.

FYI: He's taking his coaching exams.

All Change!

> *Keeps isn't the best goalkeeper ever. But he's the best goalkeeper we've got! He's been in goal for the Jags ever since we started. Maybe that's why he was fed up that night.*

Keeps   Hi, Fozzer. Where are you off to?

Fozzer   I'm going to the shops for my Mum. She's doing a goalie's special for my tea.

Keeps   What's that?

Fozzer   Beans on *post*, of course!

Keeps   That's one of the worst jokes I've ever heard.

Fozzer   Oh, I've got worse ones than that, you know. Are you going to training tonight, Keeps?

Keeps   I suppose so.

Fozzer   You sound fed up.

Keeps   Well, it's always the same. You lot take shots and I get hit in the face by the ball.

Fozzer   But it's fun. Well, it's fun for us.

Keeps   Well, it's not so much fun for me. Why can't I score goals instead of trying to stop them?

Fozzer Well, let me think. I know! Which goalkeeper can jump higher than the crossbar?

Keeps You told me that one last week. All of them can jump higher than the crossbar because crossbars can't jump.

Fozzer That's brilliant. You should tell more jokes. Crossbars can't jump! Ha, ha!

Keeps   Fozzer! It's not my joke. You were going to tell it to me, remember. And don't just make a joke about this. I mean it. I'm fed up always being in goal. Maybe I won't come to training tonight. I could stay in and watch TV instead.

Fozzer   But Keeps, you can't.

Keeps   Oh, yes, I can. And I will. I hope you have fun.

But who'll go in goal?

Team Spirit

The look on Fozzer's face got to me. I had to show up for training. But I was still fed up. Why do I always have to be in goal?

Fozzer   Keeps! You're here! Great. Go in goal, and I'll take shots at you.

Keeps   No, hang on Fozzer. Didn't you hear anything I said before?

Fozzer Of course. You told me the joke about goalies and crossbars.

Keeps No. *You* told *me* that joke. I was the one *not* laughing.

15

Fozzer   Never mind. Try this one. What is a footballer's favourite drink?

Keeps   Oh, Fozzer, I don't know. What *is* a footballer's favourite drink?

Fozzer   Penal-TEA! Like "penalty"! Get it? Good one, eh?

Keeps   Penalties are no joke to me. If I don't save them, everybody thinks I've let the team down. Like last week.

Fozzer   But that was the first one you'd let in for about a month.

Keeps   That's because we hadn't had a game for about a month. Anyway, that's not the point. The point is, I'm fed up being in goal.

Fozzer But you're our goalkeeper. What would we do without you?

Keeps Get a new goalkeeper. You could probably find someone who's better than me.

Fozzer But what would you do?

Keeps Well, maybe I'd get to score goals for once.

Fozzer What does your dad say?

Keeps   Oh, I haven't told him. I think he'd go mad. Maybe he wouldn't let me play for the Jags at all if I wasn't in goal.

Fozzer   No, Keeps. He's your dad. He only coaches the Jags because of you. I'll ask him if you like.

Keeps   Well, you can try, but I bet he'll think you're joking.

Swapping Shirts

> When the other Jags got to the Rec, I just went in goal as usual. And everybody took shots at me, as usual. But at the end, I saw Fozzer talking to my dad.

Fozzer   See, Keeps? No problem. I just asked him.

Keeps   What did you say? Did you say I don't want to go in goal any more?

Fozzer   No, Keeps. I didn't say that.

Keeps   But, Fozzer, you promised.

Fozzer   I told him *I* want to have a go in goal.

Keeps   Did you? And do you really want to have a go in goal?

Fozzer   Well, I was watching Pepe Reina in that Champions League penalty shoot-out on TV last night. He was the hero! All his team-mates mobbed him at the end. It was brilliant. The crowd were all singing his name. That could be me.

Keeps   Well, we don't get very big crowds at Jags games.

Fozzer   No, but you lot would mob me if I saved the penalty.

Keeps   Well, yes, I suppose we would, Fozzer. But what did my dad say?

Fozzer You won't believe this. He said: "I'm not sure. My son James always wants to be in goal". It's funny how he calls you James.

Keeps I know. It drives me mad.

Fozzer Anyway, he said he would talk to you about it, and we'll see on Sunday.

So, Who's Going In Goal?

There's more to Fozzer than bad jokes. I don't know if he said he'd go in goal to help me out, or because he thinks he's the next Pepe Reina.

Fozzer   Hiya, Keeps. Do I have to stop calling you that? You can't be "Keeps" if you're not the keeper, can you?

Keeps Call me what you like. Just don't call me James like my dad does. What have you got there?

Fozzer They're my goalie gloves. Well, they're not goalie gloves, really. They're the gloves my dad uses when he's cutting his roses. But they're the best I could find.

Keeps   But you won't get a feel of the ball in them. Here. Borrow mine.

Fozzer   What? Until you go back in goal?

Keeps   No, you can keep them, Fozzer. I'm a striker now.

Fozzer   What did your dad say about me going in goal?

Keeps   He said he wanted to let you have a chance, and did I mind if he put you in goal today?

Fozzer   Well, here I am. Will you give me some tips?

Keeps   Sure. What do you want to know?

Fozzer   How do you tell your team-mates you can't breathe, when they're mobbing you?

Keeps   Well, you need to make sure
you save the penalty first.

Fozzer   No problem. Let's have a go.
Where do I stand?

Keeps   Stand near the middle of the goal. But leave a bit of space to one side. The striker will hit the ball into that space. But you're already going that way. Are you ready?

Fozzer   Ready. Here comes Jim, the new striker, to take the last kick. Fozzer's in goal. Can he save this penalty to win it for Liverpool?

Keeps   Oops. That wasn't supposed to happen.

Fozzer   Never mind me being in goal. You need to practise your shooting!

Penalty!

When it got to the match, I still wasn't sure. Had I done the right thing? Was I letting the Jags down? Before we kicked off, I had a chat with Fozzer.

Fozzer   Are you all right, Keeps? I mean, Jim? Have you got your shooting boots on?

Keeps   Yeah. I hope so. I'm a bit nervous now.

Fozzer   That reminds me. What lies at the bottom of the sea and shivers? A nervous wreck!

Keeps   It's no joke, Fozzer. What if I miss a sitter?

Fozzer   What if I let one go in through my legs?

Keeps   You won't let one go in through your legs.

Fozzer   Then you won't miss a sitter, either. Good luck, mate!

Well, the game kicked off. Hill View are a good team and we did lots of defending. Fozzer made two good saves. Then I ran up the wing and passed to Jeffers. He scored!

Fozzer Goal! Goal! What a pass, Keeps!

Keeps Thanks, Fozzer. But we're only ahead because of your saves.

Fozzer I know. I'm brilliant, aren't I?

But then, the Hill View striker got free in front of our goal. Fozzer went down at his feet. Disaster! The ref gave a penalty and Fozzer was hurt.

Fozzer Ow! Hey, ref! That was never a penalty. I got the ball. Ow!

Keeps Fozzer? Are you all right?

Fozzer Ow! No. My hand hurts. Have I broken something?

Keeps No. I'm sure you're all right.

Fozzer Well, it really hurts. I can't save the spot kick. Keeps, will you go in goal?

Keeps All right, then. Just for the last few minutes. Give me my gloves back.

Fozzer Here. Quick. He's lining up the kick.

Keeps Ready, ref!

Fozzer He's saved it! He's saved it! Keeps, you're a star!

Keeps Never mind that. Let's get on with the game.

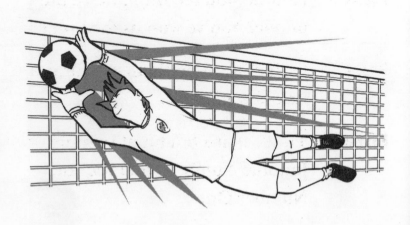

Fozzer Now do you see why you're the goalie? You've won us the game.

Keeps Only if we keep them out for the next few minutes.

Fozzer That's it, it's full-time! Jaguars, Jaguars Number One! Jaguars Number One!

Keeps Thanks, lads. Just doing my job.

Fozzer No one can do that job better, Keeps. Will you go in goal next week?

Keeps Do I have any choice? Come on the Jags!

Fozzer Come on the Jags! What a keeper!

JAGUARS 1 BURNT ASH 1

(Jags win 5–4 on penalties)

Penalty shoot-outs are a chance for the goalkeeper to be a hero. One time, we had a shoot-out in a cup game!

Nev   Come on, Keeps! It's down to you, now!

Keeps   It's not just down to me, Fozzer. You lot have to score, too.

Fozzer   Here comes Jeffers. He never misses. Goal! That's 1–0.

Keeps   My turn. Let's see what I can do.

Fozzer   Oooh! Unlucky, Keeps. Try going the right way next time.

Keeps   Thanks for the advice, Fozzer. You just go and score with your penalty now.

I did score with my penalty, of course! And I didn't really need to tell Keeps what to do. We all knew that he'd save one in the end.

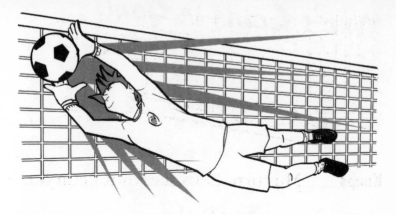

Keeps So, we're 5–4 ahead on penalties. If I save this one, the Jags will go through to the next round.

Fozzer Come on, Keeps. You can do it.

Keeps The Burnt Ash striker runs up. I think he's going to the left.

Fozzer Yesss! What a save! The Jags are through!

Who's Going in Goal?

 Some people say all goalkeepers are crazy. Maybe that's because you have to be very brave to go in goal.

 The goalkeeper is not like any other player on the pitch. He is the only player who can touch the ball with his hands. He can catch the ball or punch it or palm it away. He wears a different coloured top so everyone knows he's the person in goal.

 The goalkeeper helps the defenders on his team. Sometimes the goalkeeper shouts to the other players to tell them what to do, or warn them of danger.

 The goalkeeper also starts attacks. He can throw the ball out or kick it. Some goalkeepers have very long kicks. Some can even kick the ball all the way into the other goal!

Keeps' Quiz

Questions

1 What does a goalkeeper wear on his hands to grip the ball?

2 What can a goalkeeper do that no other player can do?

3 Why does he wear a different colour top?

4 What is a goalkeeper trying to stop the other team doing?

Answers

4 Scoring a goal.
3 So people know he's in goal.
2 Touch the ball with his hands.
1 Gloves.

About the Author

Tom Watt, who wrote the Jags books, has never been any good in goal. Maybe he's not brave enough. Maybe he can't jump high enough. Maybe he doesn't catch well enough. Maybe he can't kick the ball far enough.

Tom's son likes playing in goal. They have penalty shoot-outs in the garden. Tom usually loses. He says that's because they use a small goal! Tom and his son think Iker Casillas, the Spanish goalkeeper, is the best. Who's your favourite?

THE JAGS

Who's Got My Boots?
A New Striker
The Derby Match
Who's Washing the Kit?
The Big Deal
Star Player Wanted
Your Turn in Goal
The Team Talk
Whose Side Are You On?
Hitting the Headlines
Up for the Cup
The Own Goal

RISING★STARS